KU-662-278

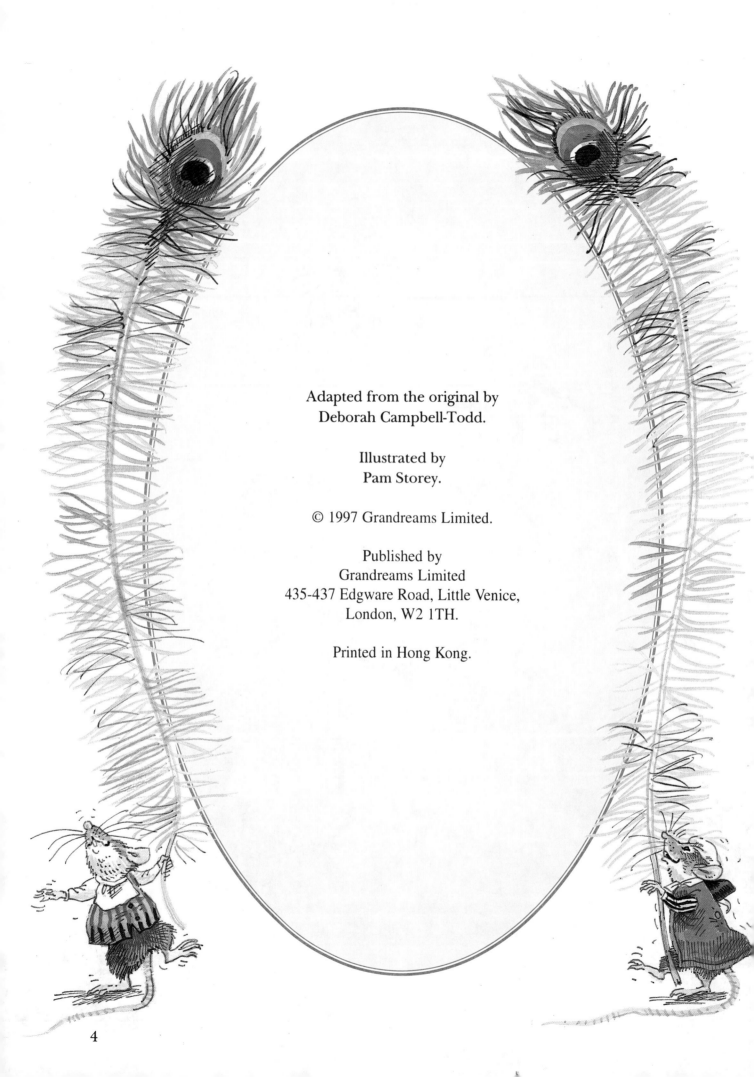

Adapted from the original by
Deborah Campbell-Todd.

Illustrated by
Pam Storey.

© 1997 Grandreams Limited.

Published by
Grandreams Limited
435-437 Edgware Road, Little Venice,
London, W2 1TH.

Printed in Hong Kong.

CONTENTS

The Town Mouse And The Country Mouse

he Town Mouse had been visiting his cousin, the Country Mouse, for a few days. The Country Mouse had his little home under a hedge on the edge of a field. The Town Mouse was now packing his bags after a very unhappy visit.

The Country Mouse watched sadly as his cousin packed.

"I feel very sorry for you," said the Town Mouse. "Life is so hard and poor for you out here in the country. All you have to eat is roots and corn."

"I like it," said the Country Mouse, looking around his little home.

"I know," said the Town Mouse. "Why don't you come and visit me? Come with me now to the town and I'll show you what good living is like!"

The Country Mouse quickly decided, and rushed to pack a bag as well. He carefully locked up his little home and the two small cousins set off.

It was a long journey to the town, and the great house where the Town Mouse lived.

The Town Mouse proudly showed his cousin around the house,

running from mousehole to mousehole. He then showed his cousin the larder by the kitchen.

The Country Mouse thought that life in the city must be wonderful indeed. Look at all this food!

"I've never seen such food!" he exclaimed to his cousin. And he started to nibble at a fig on a plate.

The larder door suddenly opened.

"Quick! Hide!" squealed the Town Mouse. "We mustn't be seen! Back into the hole!"

The two mice scurried quickly back into the Town Mouse's hole, and squashed themselves back against the wall. It was very dark and soon became very hot. The Country Mouse was most uncomfortable.

After a long time, the Town Mouse said that it was all right to move.

"I think they've gone," he said to his cousin. "We have to be careful."

The two mice moved out of the hole and stretched their legs, and tried to get the kinks out of their tails.

"I'd still like one of those," said the Country Mouse, feeling very hungry. He pointed to the plate of figs. "That little taste I had was delicious."

He crept towards the plate, and grabbed one. But before he could start eating it, the larder door opened again.

"Quick! Hide!" squealed the Town Mouse.

Dropping the fig, the Country Mouse found himself back in the Town Mouse's tiny hole, squeezed

7

tightly against his friend, with hardly room to twitch his whiskers or tail.

Again, after a long wait, his cousin said that it was safe to move.

"It may be safe now," said the Country Mouse. "But I've had enough. I'm going home. You may have good food here, and lots of it, but there's no point if you're too scared to eat it. I'll say goodbye."

The Country Mouse packed his little bag, and said farewell.

He scurried back through the town, and out into the country again. He soon found his hedge, and his little home. He happily unlocked the door and crept back into his cosy little home.

He looked around at his little home, and all his treasures "This is home for me," he said. "I like having space to twitch my nose and whiskers, and flick my tail. The Town Mouse can keep his old town!"

ur own home always seems the best to us.

The Birds, The Beasts And The Bat

t was a sad time in the animal kingdom, for the birds and the beasts were at war. The battles were fierce, and sometimes there were as many as two battles in a day.

The birds would win some battles, swooping down out of the sunny sky and attacking the animals on the ground. On other occasions, the animals would win, leaping and attacking the birds as they searched for food, or for materials for their nests.

Neither side seemed to be winning the war.

But there was one little creature who always seemed to be on the winning side of a battle. This was because he kept on changing sides. If he was fighting with the birds, and they looked like losing, he would suddenly switch sides, and join the animals. Then, after fighting with the animals, if they suddenly looked like being the losing side he would switch his loyalties and join the birds' side again.

The little creature was the bat. "I'm just so clever," he said to himself one day. "With my wings I can be with the birds, and with my body I can be with the beasts. I can be on the winning side, no matter what." He thought he was being very clever, always being on the winning side. Finally the day came when the war was brought to an end. It had gone on for far too long and too many birds and beasts had been hurt. They decided to live in peace from that day on.

The bat was pleased. "Now I shall be recognised at last, and receive a reward," he said happily. "After all, I

was never on the losing side. If anything, I helped both sides. Both the birds and the beasts must be thinking what a fine fellow I am. If I have impressed them that much, why, they may even make me their king! Wouldn't that be an achievement!"

But the beasts and the birds were not very impressed with the bat and his high hopes. It did not work out anything like the way the bat had dreamed about. In fact, the birds and the beasts wanted nothing more to

do with him!

"You were a traitor," the birds and beasts told the amazed bat. "You weren't loyal to anyone, except yourself! You changed sides so many times in the war, that you let everyone down! We don't want anything to do with you any more."

And from that day on, the birds and the beasts turned their backs on the bat, making him an outcast, ignored by all the creatures in the animal kingdom.

 eople should be loyal and stick by their friends.

A Wolf In Sheep's Clothing

A wicked old wolf was gazing down the hillside at a flock of sheep.

He was feeling very hungry and, at that moment, very greedy.

"There are dozens of sheep in that field," he said to himself. "If I could somehow get down there amongst them, I could kill and eat as many of them as I like!"

The very thought made his mouth water, and he licked his lips in anticipation.

He sat in the shade of a large tree at the top of a hill, and started to

think. He was determined to be eating a fine meal by the end of the day!

"I know!" he said, jumping up suddenly.

He ran off down the hill and headed for the farm. The shepherd was with the sheep and would not return there until the evening, when he drove the sheep back to their pen.

The wolf scrabbled around the back of the shepherd's hut, digging through a pile of rubbish until he found what he was looking for - a tatty old sheepskin.

He wrapped himself in the sheepskin as best as he could, and then headed back up the hill for the flock of sheep. He stopped by the tree and looked at the flock for a few moments, and then wandered into the field and quietly joined the sheep.

A few of the sheep looked once or twice, but all they saw was another sheep so they paid very little attention, and the wolf was free to move amongst them. Not even the shepherd noticed the extra sheep in his flock.

"Ooh, this is so easy, "thought the wolf, in a delighted way. "I shall wait until this evening, when it is growing dark and the shepherd returns to the farm. Then I'll be able to kill the fattest of the sheep here!"

The rest of the day passed with the wolf wandering among the sheep, pretending to eat the grass. In reality he was looking over the sheep to decide which one to kill later that evening.

As the sun set, the shepherd started off for the farm, unexpectedly driving the sheep ahead of him. He drove them all, including the surprised wolf in the old sheepskin, into the pen by the hut This was where the sheep were put every night, for their safety.

The shepherd went into the farmhouse and joined his family for the dark evening.

"Now's my chance," said the wolf, again licking his lips and he looked around gleefully, having finally decided which sheep to leap on and kill.

Suddenly the door to the farmhouse opened.

"Kill the fattest one in the flock," said a voice from inside the farmhouse. "The meat will last us a few days that way."

The shepherd came straight to the pen, and pulling back the bar, he picked up his axe and grabbed hold of one of the biggest sheep in the pen.

"We need meat in the farmhouse, and as you're the biggest sheep here, you'll do," said the shepherd.

He lifted his axe and brought it crashing down on the head of the wolf in sheep's clothing, thinking that he was a sheep.

ometimes we can be just too clever for our own good.

The Beekeeper And The Bees

There once lived a beekeeper who lived in a little cottage. He had several beehives in his garden. He was a very good and kind beekeeper. He kept the bees for their honey, but when he gathered the honey every year he always made sure that he left some for the bees themselves. He never

took away all the honey, even though he loved to eat it himself.

One day, some business took him away from the cottage and the beehives in the garden. As it was a warm sunny day, the bees were also away from their hives - gathering pollen for their hives.

Someone else who liked honey was stealing through the beekeeper's garden, intent on having some of the honey himself. No-one knew who the thief was, but he was a very greedy thief. He watched and waited until the beekeeper had gone, and then went up to the beehives.

He broke open each of the hives, stealing all the honey, spilling it from his jars and pots as he ran.

Some time later, the beekeeper returned home. He looked at the bee-hives in horror.

"Oh my goodness," he cried. "Who could have done this? My poor bees! What will they think when they see their homes wrecked like this?"

He looked closer and saw that all the honey had been stolen as well. "I must try to put these back together as best I can," muttered the beekeeper.

"The bees will be back soon."

The beekeeper started his work. It was a long and sticky job, as there was honey everywhere. He tried his best to match up the pieces to rebuild the hives.

Later in the day, as the sun settled lower in the sky, the beekeeper suddenly heard a familiar sound - BZZZZZZZZ! The bees were returning!

The swarm was coming over the trees when they suddenly saw their hives. They saw the broken honeycomb and the sweet honey dripping away.

And then they saw the beekeeper picking up a piece of the honeycomb, standing amongst the ruins of their hives and immediately thought that he had done all the damage.

BZZZZZZZZZZZZZZ! stormed the angry bees. They swooped down from the sky, heading straight for the poor beekeeper.

"Ouch! Oh! No! Away!" cried the beekeeper as the bees stung him again and again. "Why do you sting me? I've always helped you and kept you safe. Why don't you go and sting the man who really did all this damage to you!"

hings are very rarely quite what they seem.

The Donkey And His Shadow

ne day a traveller decided to move on to the next town. He felt that it was a long way to walk so he would hire a donkey to carry him.

He found a man willing to hire him a donkey, and agreed the fee.

"I'm afraid that there is one drawback, however," said the donkey's owner.

"My donkey can be a bit lazy, and unless I'm there to give it a tap with a stick every so often, it tends to stop. Therefore, you ride the donkey, and I

shall walk behind with my stick. That way she will keep moving and I can ride her home again afterwards."

The traveller agreed to this, and the two men and the donkey set off.

It was a very hot day, and the traveller sat on top of the donkey, and the owner walked behind with the stick. Every so often he had to prod the donkey to keep her moving. Even though it was hot, they made good progress.

They agreed to stop at noon, when the sun was at its hottest.

The traveller got off the donkey and stretched.

"I shall sit in the shade of the donkey," he said.

"Oh no, you don't," said the donkey's owner. "It's my donkey, and it's the only shade around for miles. I shall sit in her shade and rest there."

"But I've hired the donkey," said the traveller. "Therefore I should sit

in her shade."

"But that's the point," said the owner. "You've only paid for the donkey. You haven't paid for her shadow! That's still mine!"

The owner and the traveller continued to argue, and they grew more and more angry.

Finally the owner pushed the traveller. The traveller pushed back.

Then the owner hit the traveller, and the traveller hit the owner back.

It was not long before the two men were involved in a furious fist fight, in the middle of the dusty road, in the heat of the midday sun.

Meanwhile, the donkey had grown bored with the two men. She had chewed for a time at some grass, but now had decided to go her own way.

She therefore trotted off down the road, away from the two men. She was soon out of sight - and she had taken her shadow with her.

 ost arguments are useless.

The Lark And The Farmer

 n Springtime when the birds start to build their nests, most birds build their nests in trees or in cliffs. They like to keep their homes above the ground, and above our heads and hopefully out of danger.

There is one bird however, that likes to build its nest on the ground. And that is the lark. She likes to make her home for her babies in the middle of the cornfield. She feels that she is just as safe here as on a tree.

After all, once the corn is growing, no-one is going to damage the corn by walking through the middle of the field.

The lark made her nest, laid her eggs and waited for them to hatch. Soon she had three little babies to look after and they kept her busy all the Spring. Meanwhile the corn grew higher and higher around them.

The Summer passed by, in lovely sunny days, and the mother lark watched her babies grow their

feathers and start to leave the nest.

The mother lark would spend hours singing above the field, telling her children about what she could see from her great height. The children listened to her and looked forward to when they could fly with her.

One day, the farmer who owned the field came walking by and stopped to consider the corn.

"This is just about ready," he said out loud. "I think it's time to have a word with the neighbours and ask them to help me gather it in."

"Mother! Mother!" cried the young larks from the nest. "We must go! Our little home will be destroyed!" The little birds were very scared.

"Hush, little ones," said the mother lark, flying down to the nest to soothe her young children. "We need not worry yet. The farmer is only talking of asking his neighbours to help. He can be in no great hurry to gather his corn in at the moment. We have some time to wait."

The warm days passed, and the mother lark could see that the corn was so ripe it was falling over. By now her babies were flying with her, but they still liked to spend their nights in the little nest on the ground. The farmer returned to his field, and felt the corn and looked around.

"Now's the time! I must hire some men to help me cut this corn at once!" he said.

"Now, little ones, is the time to move," said the mother lark to her children. "The farmer has now made a decision and is acting on it. He's relying on himself and not his neighbours. We must fly away."

 f we want something, it is usually best to do it ourselves.

The Hound And The Lion

 ne day, a hound decided to visit the jungle.

"I'll see what I can find there," he said to himself, as he set off.

Now, the hound had never been in the jungle before, and he knew very little about the creatures that lived there. But this didn't worry him. Where he lived, everyone thought that he was a great and brave hunter. Nothing scared him after all, he had chased and killed many animals, so surely there would be nothing in the jungle that could possibly scare him.

He walked on, and suddenly saw an animal in front of him on the path.

It was a lion. The hound had never seen a lion before, but that did not worry him at all.

"I'll soon catch him," thought the hound, and he followed the lion down the path.

He followed the lion for a while, and then he broke into a trot. He was just getting ready to leap on the beast.

Something made him pause.

The lion stopped and turned round, just as the hound drew level with him.

The lion stared at the hound.

The hound suddenly realised that the beast in front of him was bigger, stronger and more dangerous than any animal he had faced before.

The two animals stared at each other for a moment, and then the lion opened his mouth and let out a mighty roar!

The hound was terrified. He had never heard such a frightening sound! The roar echoed back and forth between the trees, setting off other animal cries.

The hound couldn't move! He was so scared!

He looked at the lion in front of him, and saw for the first time the sharp and savage teeth! He saw the strong shoulders and great paws and long, tearing claws!

A moment later, the hound turned and ran!

He ran as fast as he could possibly go, dashing along the jungle paths.

All he wanted to do was to put as much of the jungle between himself and the fierce beast with the dreadful teeth and claws and that frightening roar!

A fox had been watching the hound, and seeing his panic and the speed he was running, laughed out loud.

"It didn't take much to make you run, did it, my friend?" he called out to the swiftly disappearing hound.

The hound did not stop or even look back.

e should find out as much as possible about someone before coming into conflict with him.

The Quack Frog

here was once a frog who lived beside a small stream. He spent all his day croaking to himself and to anyone else who would listen. When he wasn't croaking, he was catching flies for his food.

Needless to say, the frog was very bored.

"There must be more I can do," said the frog to himself.

He thought things over for a few days, and then decided that he must move into a nearby town to make his fortune.

"I shall become a doctor," he finally decided. "But not an ordinary doctor. I shall become a quack doctor!" A quack doctor is not a real doctor, but one who claims he can cure all known ills with a single medicine.

The frog took up a stall in the market, and that evening collected as many bottles as he could. These he filled with pond water and bits of grass and plants growing by the pond.

"This is my cure-all!" announced the frog proudly.

The next day, he started to set out the multitude of bottles he had. There were green ones, blue ones,

clear and brown ones. Some had screw tops, some had corks or rubber bungs. Everyone was different, but the contents were the same.

Finally he was ready, and he was

happy with the way his stall looked.

"Come one, come all!" he called to the crowds of animals in the market. "Bring me your ails and your troubles. Tell me what is wrong with you and I can promise I shall have a cure in my bottles! Do you have aching joints or bald patches? You'll find the cure for everything in the magical contents of my bottles!"

A crowd of animals was by now standing in front of the frog's stall.

"I'll have some of that!" cried a duck.

"So will I," called a sheep.

The animals rushed up to buy the

bottles of medicine.

In the middle of the crowd, a fox stood watching the frog.

"You say you can cure anything with this medicine," he called out. "Are you sure?"

"Of course," said the frog, lying all the time. "I will have you know that I have studied with some of the best doctors in the country. My magical medicine can cure any ailment!"

At this statement, the animals pressed forward, wanting to buy the magical medicine.

The fox watched as bottle after bottle left the shelf, and then he considered the 'doctor'.

"If," he called out in a soft voice, "you are such a great and clever doctor, can you tell us why you cannot walk. Why do you jump if you have such wonderful medicine? Why is your skin so wrinkled and blotchy?"

The other animals stopped and looked, considering what the fox had said, and then found that they had to agree with him.

Why was the doctor blotchy and wrinkled, why couldn't he walk?

Of course, there was no answer from the frog.

The animals jeered and booed at the frog. They demanded he took his bottles of medicine back and give back all the money.

The frog sadly gave back all the money, and then hopped away from his market stall, returning to his pool. And there he sits, croaking away.

 octor, heal yourself.

The Fox And The Crow

t had been a long day for the fox, and he was feeling very hungry. He walked through the fields and into the woods, looking left and right for food.

"I could eat anything," he said to himself. And then he suddenly realised what he fancied more than anything else in the world. "Cheese!" he exclaimed. "I'd love even just a small lump of cheese! That would really be something delicious, a real treat!"

The fox was walking past some trees as the cheesy thought came flashing into his mind, and he looked up when he heard the branches rustling.

There, in the branches, was a crow. And in her beak - was a piece of cheese!

The fox's mouth watered, and he licked his lips.

"Now, how can I get that cheese from the crow?" he asked himself. He settled himself down on the ground, wrapping his great bushy tail around his feet, thinking all the while. He looked up at the crow.

"Oh, dear friend Crow," he said admiringly. He smiled sweetly, as though butter would not melt in his mouth. "You are such a beautiful bird. The sun is shining on your black feathers in such a way that it is making them gleam like some precious stone. And the curve of your beak gives you such

an elegant look."

The crow listened to the fox, wondering what he would say next. She was enjoying all the kind words.

"You are so beautiful," said the fox. "If only..."

The crow turned her head. If only ... If only what?

The fox was shaking his head and the crow listened to hear what the fox was going to say.

"If only your voice was a beautiful as the rest of you," said the fox. "Surely you would then be a queen among all the birds."

The crow was greatly flattered, but thought to herself, "I can sing, and I'll show the fox that I can."

She opened her beak, and gave a loud caw to show off her beautiful voice.

The piece of cheese tumbled from her beak, falling down to the ground where the fox sat waiting.

The fox jumped up, picked up the cheese and off he ran, not looking back, thinking of the little feast he had just won.

 eware of flattery, it may not be meant.

The Two Pots

t seemed to have been raining for days, and all the water was rushing off the fields, sweeping branches and rubbish into the river at the bottom of the valley.

The river was therefore high in flood. Bobbing along in the fast-moving water were two pots, helpless and unable to leave the water until they were driven into the riverbanks.

One of the pots was a beautiful shiny pot made from a mixture of metals, known as brass. The other pot was just as beautiful, but it was nowhere near as strong, as it was made of clay.

The brass pot spotted the clay pot

bobbing along beside it, and called out to it. "Why don't you come closer to me?" it asked. "I'm very strong. I will look after you. I might dent a little, but nothing can break me."

The clay pot looked over at the brass pot, and tried to make the gap between them bigger.

"Don't do that!" said the brass pot. "I can look after you. I know you clay pots are a lot weaker than us. Let me protect you!" And he looked as though he would try and catch the clay pot.

"No, really!" called out the clay pot, staying as far from the brass pot as possible. "It's very kind of you. But I'd rather be on my own."

"Why?" asked the brass pot, who was really a little hurt to be turned down. "I only wanted to help."

"I know you mean well," said the clay pot, "but as you say, you are brass and I am clay and you are much stronger than me. Just think, one small accidental tap from you, and I would be shattered into a thousand pieces!"

The brass pot had to agree.

 quals make the best friends.

The Spendthrift And The Swallow

here was once a man who inherited a great deal of money from a long distant relative.

He was not used to such an amount of money and could not believe his good fortune.

"What can I buy first?" he asked himself. "With this much money I need never worry again!"

He started to spend his now vast fortune, buying clothes and trips to the theatre for himself and his friends. He dined in all the expensive places, being seen in the smartest clothes with the smartest of friends. Unfortunately he did not put any money away to save for a rainy day. He became a spendthrift - spending every single penny that the distant relative had left him. Money does not last forever when it is spent in such a fashion, and soon the foolish man had spent all his money. He didn't have a penny to his name. All he possessed were the clothes he stood up in.

"Ah well," he said "Why should I worry? I had no money before and I managed. I'll get by. Something good will happen and everything will be alright."

Spring had arrived, and he was walking along a narrow country lane.

"What a lovely morning," said the man. "It's sunny and warm. I'll just stroll along here and see what the day brings."

As he walked along, he glanced up at the sky and saw a single bird swooping and diving through the air.

"What's that?" he cried. "Why it's a swallow! A swallow now can only mean one thing - summer is on its way. That means that there are more swallows on the way! Summer is definitely here!"

The man took of his coat, slung it over his arm and carried on his way to the next village, whistling with every step he took. He knew that summer was on the way.

"If summer is almost here," said the man, thinking out loud. "Then I don't need my coat any more. I can sell it and buy some food instead."

With that intention, the man went to the inn and sold his coat for a meal and some bread and cheese to take away with him.

"Summer is almost here, you see," he told the landlord, who found the coat fitted quite well. "I shan't be

needing this any more."

"Let's hope you're right, sir," said the landlord, as he ladled out a generous helping of stew and a jar of ale.

After his meal the man set out again, strolling in the afternoon sun.

But the next day, the weather had turned against him. The wind changed direction, the clouds covered the sky and it turned bitterly cold.

It was cold enough to kill some of the birds and animals who had also thought that spring was over. Snow came down, and the man was freezing without his coat.

As he looked for somewhere to shelter, he came across the frozen body of the swallow.

He looked at the bird, and declared bitterly, "I sold my coat because of you! And look at me now - I'm freezing!"

 ne swallow does not make a summer.

The Mice In Council

There was once a community of mice with a very large problem.

That problem had four feet, long whiskers, a long tail, large teeth and sharp claws. It was a cat! And the cat was terrorising the mice, catching and killing as many as she could.

Word passed among the mice that there was to be a great council in the hole beside the fireplace. Some way had to be found to protect themselves from the cat!

Many mice braved the journey to the meeting place and the council lasted a long time. Many suggestions were put forward, and rejected as impossible to carry out.

Suddenly, a bright young mouse had a thought. He stepped forward.

"I have an idea!" he called out. "Why are so many of us caught by the cat?"

"Because she's fast!" called one.

"Because she's hungry!" called another.

"But it's also because she's so quiet!" said the young mouse. "We just don't hear her coming, do we?"

"We realise that, but it doesn't help much," said a mouse.

"Wait a moment, I've had an idea," continued the young mouse. "If we are to avoid being caught, we must hear her coming. We need a warning noise, Well, I've worked out

"What do you think?"

"It's a brilliant idea!" cried several of the mice.

"I think I know where to find a bell," said one. "You've solved our problem. Well done!" He dashed up to the hole looking out into the room, only to see the cat on the other side lazing in the sun.

The other mice were clapping the bright young mouse, convinced that their problems were over.

A wise old mouse suddenly stood up. He had not said anything so far at the council.

"Ahem!" he coughed, attracting the attention of the other mice. "This may be a good idea, but there is one thing I would like to know."

"Yes?" asked the bright young mouse.

"Once you have the bell, is there anybody here who is willing to risk his life in trying to put the bell around the cat's neck?" he asked.

There was no answer. The mice looked at each other, waiting for someone else to volunteer. Nobody was prepared to put the bell on the cat, and within a few moments the hole by the fireplace was cleared of mice as they all made their way from the meeting.

what to do. We must tie a bell around her neck, and then when she's anywhere near us, we'll be able to hear her and then we can all get away!"

t's no use having good ideas, unless we are prepared to put them into practice.

The Man And The Satyr

A satyr is a wood god. He is half man and half goat. One satyr, many years ago, used to live with a man in a small cottage on the edge of a forest. The satyr liked to stay close to his original home, the forest.

The two had lived together for a few years and got on really well,

sharing the chores and tasks around the house.

One winter, the weather was particularly cold, much colder than they were used to, and the two were out one day collecting wood for the fire.

The man suddenly stopped what he was doing, took off his gloves and began to blow on his frozen fingers.

"What are you doing?" asked the satyr, much puzzled by the man's actions.

"Blowing on my fingers," said the man, surprised at the question.

"But why are you blowing on them?" asked the satyr.

"To warm them up, or course," said the man. "The best way to warm up cold fingers is to blow on them. Didn't you know that?"

The satyr shook his head in a puzzled way, and carried on collecting the wood,

Later on, inside the cottage, with a blazing fire going, the man decided to cook a stew for their supper.

Evening fell and it was dark and snowing again outside. The man and the satyr sat down at the table to eat the hot stew.

The man put out two bowls of the stew, but when he raised his spoon he found that his was too hot.

He suddenly began to blow on the stew in the spoon and in the bowl.

The satyr looked on in amazement.

"What are you doing now?" he asked the man.

"Blowing on my stew," said the man. "What does it look like?"

"But why are you blowing on it?" asked the satyr.

"Because it is too hot!" exclaimed the man. "It's much too hot to eat at the moment!"

The satyr pushed back his chair, standing up. He shook his head slowly.

"I don't understand this at all," he said. "I'm off."

"Off! But where are you going? Why do you want to go?" asked the man. "What's wrong?"

"I am going back to the forest," said the satyr, heading for the door. "I want to get as far away as possible from someone who can blow hot and cold with the same breath!"

eople like us to remain constant and to do the same things all the time.

The Peacock And The Crane

There was once a peacock who was extremely vain and proud.

He spent all his time admiring himself, and boasting to the other birds about how beautiful he was.

"Just look at my beautiful feathers," he would say, turning this way and that, showing off his long feathers. "Look at the colours in my tail! Looking at them I imagine that I must be the most beautiful bird in the world! Nobody else can possibly have feathers like mine!"

When it rained, he could fold up his tail feathers. But as soon as it stopped and the sun came out, he would open his tail like a fan and stand admiring the colours of his tail in his reflection in the puddles. He would wait for someone to come by in the hopes that they would stand and admire him.

The other birds were becoming more than a little tired of the peacock's constant boasting.

"What can we do?" they said to each other. "He needs to be taught a lesson."

One day, the crane had an idea.

He was quite a large bird, taller than the peacock, and like the other birds had become bored with the peacock.

"I think I know what to do," said the crane to the other birds. "He'll soon feel very foolish."

A short while later, the peacock was strolling past the trees where some of the birds were sitting. As usual he was preening his feathers and admiring himself.

The crane flew down and walked past him.

"Oh crane," said the foolish peacock. "Just look at the way the sun is shining on my feathers this morning. Don't I look just wonderful?"

The crane said nothing.

"You know something, Crane," said the peacock, with a swish of his tail. "You really should try and smarten yourself up. You do look a little dull."

The crane looked at the peacock.

"Your feathers may be more beautiful than mine, peacock," began the crane.

And the peacock shook his tail, and preened a little.

"But I noticed that you cannot fly," continued the crane. "Your feathers may be very beautiful down here on the ground but they are not strong enough to carry you into the air. But my dull feathers can carry me up into the sky and far away."

And the crane took off, leaving the peacock feeling very silly.

We may lose in one way, but we can gain in another.

The Trees And The Axe

There was once a great forest that covered many miles.

One day a woodsman went to the forest. He looked around and saw the great trees. They were tall and strong. Some of them had been in the forest for hundreds of years.

The man stopped in the middle of a clearing, and cleared his throat.

The trees stopped their rustling and bustling to hear what the woodsman had to say.

"I must apologise for disturbing you," he said, in a loud voice, so that many of the trees could hear him. He faced the biggest and oldest of the trees. "I realise that you great trees must be the kings of the forest."

There was a little rustle at his words.

"I have a favour to ask," he said. "I've broken the handle on my axe, and I wondered if I might be able to cut down a tree and make a new handle. Obviously, I don't mean one of you great trees! All it would take is just a small one. Is there a small tree, somewhere?"

The great trees, the kings of the forest, rustled and muttered together.

They had never been spoken to in such a polite way, and they were most impressed. They nodded their great heads, rustling and shivering their leaves as they did.

"You have asked in such a kind way, and after all, you are not asking for too much," said the trees. "Yes, you may cut down one small tree. There is a young sapling over there."

The woodsman looked between the trees, and saw a young ash tree. It was not very tall or very thick. It was perfect for his purposes.

"Thank you all, so much," said the woodsman, bowing to the great trees.

He walked quickly over to the small tree before the larger trees could change their minds. With his broken axe, he very quickly cut down the small thin tree.

Then he sat and worked the piece of wood into a new handle for his axe. Then he sat and started to sharpen the blade of the axe.

Shortly the trees knew the real reason for his coming to the forest.

He picked up his newly repaired and now sharp axe and began to cut at the trees in front of him.

He cut them all down, big and small, young and old. He cut a path through the forest, leaving branches and fallen trees behind him. He then started to cut the wood into logs.

Before long, most of the forest had been cut down. A few trees still stood, greatly regretting the way they had welcomed the man, and even more regretting the way they had given up the first ash tree. All for

some flattery by the man.

"It is all our own fault!" they cried. "We brought about the death of ourselves and the forest. We shouldn't have let the woodsman cut down that first small ash tree. We should have protected that little tree and then we would have been protecting ourselves!"

 nity is strength.

The Fox
And The Stork

here was once a fox who lived in the forest. He had a friend who lived out by the water on the river's edge. She was a stork.

The fox was fond of playing tricks on the stork, and one day he invited her for dinner in his cave.

"I would be so pleased if you would come," said the fox to the stork, as they talked at the edge of the forest. All the while he was thinking of the joke he was going to play on her.

"That's very kind of you, I would be delighted," said the stork with a smile, not suspecting anything of the fox.

The stork arrived at the fox's cave, and was invited in to the table.

The fox served up a delicious smelling soup, but he served it on a very flat dish.

"This really is quite tasty," he said to the stork, as he lapped at the soup, with his nose just a few inches from the dish. "Why don't you try some?" he asked slyly.

"I would if I could," said the stork, crossly. "But I cannot lap from a dish the way you do. And I cannot get any by pecking at the dish."

This was exactly as the fox had known, and he was delighted with the joke. He had made the stork look silly and upset her at the same time - and it was so easy! He thought this was very funny, and smiled all the time he finished lapping up the soup.

"That was lovely," he said, licking his lips.

The stork tried to peck a couple more times, but it was no use and eventually she left the smiling fox and went back to her home by the river, determined to get her own back on the fox.

A few days later, an invitation arrived for the fox to dine with the stork.

"I would be delighted," sniggered the fox. He knew the stork was a good cook, and was sure that she had seen the funny side of things and would cook something really tasty for them.

The fox arrived at the stork's home and was shown to the table.

The stork had certainly been busy. She too had made soup, but this time it was served in a jug. The jug had a narrow neck, and opened out into a large bowl.

"Now that you've arrived, we can start," said the stork, putting the jug on the table.

She dipped her beak into the jug and took a long sip.

"Mmm, tasty," she said. "Won't you try some, my friend?"

"How can I?" muttered the fox. "I can't get my head in there. It does smell good! But I can't reach to lap it and taste it."

"No?" said the stork. "That is a shame. I really do think it is one of my best yet!"

She carried on sipping up the soup, until the jug was empty. The fox could only look on.

In the end, he decided to go home. He was very annoyed that the same joke had been played on him - and he didn't find it funny.

 omething that seems amusing when it happens to someone else, does not seem quite so funny when it happens to us.

The Fortune Teller

t was the first Wednesday of the month, which meant that it was market day in the small town. Farmers and traders had come from miles around to sell their wares.

There was noise everywhere. The sheep, cattle and pigs were bleating, lowing and grunting. The chickens were squawking, the ducks were quacking and the turkeys were gobbling. Farmers were calling to each other to pass on news and greetings from their wives.

Traders were dealing in butters and cheeses, fish and meats. The baker and the butcher had their shops open, selling their breads and pies. Market stalls were selling materials and ribbons for the farmers to take back to their wives. Some wives who had come in with their farmer husbands were busy looking at the hats and dress materials on sale. Market day was only once a month, after all!

In the midst of all this noise, there stood a fortune teller.

He was dressed in a long cloak that covered his clothes. He had a long beard and he wore a little hat on his head which made him look very mysterious.

People were handing over coins to hear the man tell them what the future held for them, and he was

doing a roaring trade.

Farmer's wives were his main audience, but there were some children and one or two men lingered to hear what he had to say.

"Ooh!" said one woman, as he told her something that would happen to her within the next few weeks. "Fancy that!" she declared.

"Tell me something," said another.

"I'd like to hear my fortune, too," said someone else, tugging on his sleave, with a gold coin held out.

"I shall tell you all," said the fortune teller, taking the person's money. "I shall be here all day!"

As the fortune teller began to tell the woman's future, a boy arrived at the crowd around him. He began to shove and push his way through the people.

"Hold on there, youngster," said a man. "Wait your turn."

"Stand still, lad!" bellowed the fortune teller. "You cannot push to the front. There are others in front of you. I shall get to you eventually. Have you a penny?"

"But, sir," said the boy, still pushing his way through.

"I said to wait," repeated the fortune teller in a loud voice. "Now my dear, where was I?" he said more gently to the woman in front of him.

"But I came to tell you the news," said the boy, trying to be heard.

"What news? What are you on about?" said the fortune teller.

"Thieves have broken into your house," panted the boy. "They've broken down the door and got in and stolen everything!"

"What did you say?" roared the

fortune teller, turning scarlet in the face.

"I said, you've been broken into. Thieves have stolen everything you own," said the boy again.

The fortune teller threw up his hands in dismay, and fighting his way through the crowd of people, he ran across the market square, past the busy stalls and into the street leading to his home.

"Well," said the woman who had been having her fortune read.

The rest of the crowd looked after the fortune teller in amazement, shaking their heads.

"Strange, isn't it," said one of the crowd after a few moments. "He was standing there telling us exactly what was going to happen to us, and yet he couldn't see for himself that his own house was being broken into!"

e sure your own house is in order before giving advice to others

The Stag At The Pool

 here was once a fine stag that lived in the forest.

It was a lovely spring day and he was at the pool in the forest, taking a drink.

When he had drunk enough he looked at his reflection in the water. He looked at the fine set of antlers he now had.

"They really are very fine antlers," he said proudly to himself, turning his head this way and that, and admiring his reflection. "They make me look a very handsome stag."

He started to turn away, but as he did he looked at the rest of himself and stopped again.

He looked at his legs, which were very slim and elegant, and decided that they were not so fine after all.

"It's such a pity," he said, looking down at his legs. "My legs are so thin. Why can't they be more like my antlers. Maybe I can do something to

the way, and fled. The ground ahead was open and clear of trees, and the stag ran and ran.

The stag's legs were much longer than the lion's and they served the stag well. The stag was soon far ahead of the lion.

The stag decided to dash into the forest to find somewhere to hide. He dashed in among the trees, leaping left and right.

But the trees grew low over the path, and unfortunately the stag's antlers became entangled in the branches, trapping him. The stag was forced to stop, and within moments the lion had caught up with him.

"Oh, I am such a fool!" cried the stag, as the lion leapt on him. "The legs that I have despised have served me so well! And the antlers that I admired so greatly have swiftly brought about my downfall."

improve them?"

At that moment, a lion that had been following the stag, came running up. It was ready to leap on the stag!

The stag jumped up and out of

hat is worth the most is often valued least.

Jupiter And The Tortoise

T he tortoise has not always carried his home around with him. Indeed, thousands of years ago, the tortoise lived in a little house just like any other creature. The roof was domed and he was very houseproud and kept the whole house very tidy.

But one day something happened that made sure the tortoise and his home would be together forever.

The great god Jupiter decided to hold an enormous feast. He invited all the animals he knew to this feast. And every living beast turned up to the feast, and had a wonderful time. All the animals came, apart from one - and that was the tortoise.

Now Jupiter was very disappointed. He was a very generous and kind god, and was most upset that not every single creature under the sun was there. It would then have been such a great feast!

"I wonder why he didn't come?" said Jupiter to himself. "Maybe I do him an injustice - he might be ill? I shall go and call on him, to see that he is all right."

Jupiter was so worried about the tortoise, that he went straight away to see him.

"Maybe he's hurt himself, and he couldn't make the journey," worried the god as he hurried to the tortoise's house. He picked up his speed to get there even quicker.

Jupiter arrived at the field where the tortoise had built his house.

He knocked on the door, and waited patiently for the tortoise to open the door. The tortoise was there a few moments later.

Jupiter was very surprised to see that the tortoise looked very well. There was nothing wrong with him at all.

"I invited you to my feast," said

Jupiter. "It was today. Didn't you receive my invitation?"

"Yes I did, thank you," said the tortoise slowly.

"Then why didn't you come?" asked the god. "I wanted all the animals to be there, and you were the only one who didn't turn up. I thought you were ill or something had happened to you."

"No I'm perfectly all right," said the tortoise, with a yawn.

"Then why didn't you come?" asked the god again.

"To be honest," said the tortoise. "I didn't really feel like it."

"Didn't feel like it!" said the god.

"No, I was warm and cosy here," said the tortoise. "And I thought it looked like rain when I looked out of the window. I changed my mind and decided to stay at home instead."

"Is that right?" said Jupiter, feeling quite angry. "In that case, if you are so fond of staying at home, from now until the end of time, you may as well carry your home around with you!"

To the tortoise's surprise he suddenly found his home shrinking around his ears, until it fitted neatly on his back.

From that day on, he carried his home as a shell everywhere with him. And Jupiter will not change things back for him.

And when it rains, the tortoise finds he can just get his feet and head inside.

 e should be careful of what we say, in case we are taken at our word.

The Boy And The Wolf

 young boy was walking out in the fields near to his village. He was on his own, looking for something different to do. School had finished for the afternoon, and his friends had all gone home.

Also out walking in the fields was a wolf. He also was looking for something to do.

The young boy saw the wolf before the wolf saw him.

"I must hide from him," he said to himself. "I'm too far from home. I'm just not fast enough to get away from him." And he dropped down into some long grass and tried to hide from the wolf.

The wolf crossed the boy's path and could immediately smell him. He found the boy's hiding place in no time at all. He stood in front of the boy, with his teeth bared.

"Oh, please, Mr. Wolf," pleaded the boy, "please don't eat me!" He shook with fright.

The wolf stopped a moment. When he found the boy, he had at once decided to kill and eat him. But on second thoughts, he really had had enough to eat that day. He had already killed many small animals and was not at all hungry.

"I think I shall have some fun with this frightened little boy instead," thought the wolf.

"Very well," he growled, licking his lips to scare the boy even more. "You can walk away from here with your life, if you can tell me three things."

"What three things?" asked the boy.

"Three things that are so true, that I cannot possibly disagree with you," said the wolf.

The boy began to think quickly, his life would depend on his answers

"Well, firstly," he began. "It is really a great shame that you saw me."

"That's true enough," said the wolf. "Now, two more answers are needed."

"Secondly," said the boy, slowly. "It's a great shame that I let you find me."

"I'll agree with that," said the wolf. "That's two answers. Now, what is your third answer to be?"

"Thirdly," said the boy, very quickly, "people hate wolves because they will attack and kill sheep for no reason at all."

The wolf was silent for a moment, considering the boy's answer. The boy waited, silently, wondering if he had been too bold.

"I suppose that is true from your point of view," said the wolf, tilting his head to one side, having given due consideration. He was a very fair-minded wolf, and did not go back on his word.

"Very well," he said. "You may go!"

And off the boy ran!

 fair-minded person will try to see both sides of an argument.

The Travellers And The Plane Tree

he two travellers were on their way to the large town. They had left their small village very early that morning as it was such a long walk. It had been cool and misty when they left, but the sun had soon broken through, and was now beating down on them out of a clear blue sky.

They were getting hotter and hotter, and one man mopped at his face with his handkerchief.

"How much further is the town?" he said to his friend. "I'll need to rest soon if this heat continues."

"It's not much further," said the other. "We'll find a shady place and sit for a few minutes."

But as they looked around there were no shady places to be seen.

"Let's keep going," said the first traveller. "We can't stay here."

The two men stripped off their coats and carried on walking.

Still the sun shone down on them.

They slowly climbed a low hill and, when they reached the top, there in the distance was a tree! It was the only tree for miles around.

"At last!" cried the travellers.

"Some shade!"

The two travellers hurried as best they could up to the tree. As they drew closer they saw it was a plane tree.

The great tree spread its branches out and offered welcome shade to the two men.

They both sighed out loud as they sank to the grass beneath the cool shade of the tree.

"Aah!' sighed one. "Thank goodness we found this tree. I couldn't have gone much further in this heat."

"We can have a snack and a drink in comfort," said the other.

The two men dozed a little in the cooling shade of the plane tree, and after a while opened their bags to have something to eat.

One of the men stopped halfway through his sandwich. "It's funny, you know," he said, looking up at the tree.

"What's funny?" asked the other.

"Well, this plane tree we're sitting under."

"What about it?"

"Well have you ever considered just how useless it is?" said the first

traveller, still looking up at the tree.

"What do you mean - useless?"

"Just think about it. It doesn't blossom, so it isn't a pretty tree to look at in the spring, like an apple or pear tree. And it doesn't give any kind of fruit or nut so man gets nothing from it."

The second man looked up as well. "You're right. It's a pretty useless tree."

The plane tree overhead listened to their conversation.

"What ungrateful people!" thought the tree angrily. "They were more than happy to see me in the first place, when they were being roasted by the sun. Just think how they ran to reach me! And now they're more than happy to sit in my shade. But I don't hear either of them saying thank you. Instead they lie there in this shade and coolness, out of the blazing sun, and have the cheek to complain that I am useless!"

 e're not always grateful for help when it is offered.

The Pig
And The Sheep

here was once a pig who lived in a sty along with lots of other pigs. He decided he did not like life in the sty,

and one day he started to make plans for his escape.

He had seen the sheep out in the fields, and decided that this was the

kind of life he wanted.

One day, when the farmer came to feed the pigs, the pig rushed out through the gate past the farmer.

"Here, stop!" called the farmer after him. "Where do you think you're going?"

"To a different home," said the pig to himself, as he rushed off through the farmyard.

He raced out into the fields, and joined the flock of sheep he had seen.

The sheep did not mind him, and soon made friends with the pig. He was very happy to be out of his sty.

The days passed pleasantly for the pig, out in the sunshine. And he did not even mind when it rained. He was out of his sty and that was the important thing!

One day, the farmer went through the field, to see his sheep, and he spotted the pig. But unfortunately, the pig did not see him. Moments later the pig was tucked under the farmer's arm!

"Off with you to the butcher!" said the farmer to the pig.

The pig squealed and squealed. He wriggled and squirmed, trying desperately to get out of the farmer's arms. The sheep looked on in amazement.

"What on earth is the matter?" they asked. "Why are you making such a fuss? We don't struggle like that when the farmer picks us up!"

"No, you probably don't," said the pig, squirming and struggling to escape. "But then he wants a lot more from me than he does from you. All he wants from you is your wool. But with me, he wants my bacon!"

 e should not make up our minds about something until we know the truth.